Spring Harvest
Bible Workbook

COLOSSIANS

Big Themes from Colossians

Authentic

Equipping the Church for action

Copyright © 2002 Elizabeth McQuoid

First published in 2002 by Spring Harvest Publishing Division and Authentic Lifestyle

10 09 08 07 06 05 04   8 7 6 5 4 3 2

Reprinted in 2004 by Authentic Media
9 Holdom Avenue, Bletchley, Milton Keynes, Bucks., MK1 1QR, UK
and P.O. Box 1047, Waynesboro, GA 30830-2047, USA
www.authenticmedia.co.uk

British Library Cataloguing in Publication Data

A catalogue record for this book is available from the British Library

ISBN 1-85078-457-4

Typeset by Spring Harvest
Printed in Great Britain by Bell and Bain Ltd., Glasgow

CONTENTS

ABOUT THIS BOOK

The aim of this study guide is to examine the big issues that Paul addressed when he wrote to the Colossian Christians. These issues are still relevant today and will challenge us to make sure of what we believe and that it relates to our lives, seven days a week.

This book is written primarily for a group situation, but can easily be used by individuals who want to study the big themes from Colossians. It can be used in a variety of contexts, so it is perhaps helpful to spell out the assumptions that we have made about the groups that will use it. These can have a variety of names – homegroups, Bible study groups, cell groups – we've used housegroup as the generic term.

▶ The emphasis of the studies will be on the application of the Bible. Group members will not just learn facts, but will be encouraged to think 'How does this apply to me? What change does it require of me? What incidents or situations in my life is this relevant to?'

▶ Housegroups can encourage honesty and make space for questions and doubts. The aim of the studies is not to find the right answer, but to help members understand the Bible by working through their questions. The Christian faith throws up paradoxes. Events in people's lives may make particular verses difficult to understand. The housegroup should be a safe place to express these concerns.

▶ Housegroups can give opportunities for deep friendships to develop. Group members can be encouraged to talk about their experiences, feelings, questions, hopes and fears. They are able to offer one another pastoral support and to get involved in each other's lives.

▶ There is a difference between being a collection of individuals who happen to meet together every Wednesday and being an effective group who bounce ideas off each other, spark inspiration and creativity, pooling their talents and resources to create solutions together: one whose whole is definitely greater than the sum of its parts. The process of working through these studies will encourage healthy group dynamics.

Space is given for you to write answers, comments, questions and thoughts. This book will not tell you what to think, but will help you discover the truth of God's word through thinking, discussing, praying and listening.

FOR GROUP MEMBERS

▶ You will probably get more out of the study if you spend some time during the week reading the passage and thinking about the questions. Make a note of anything you don't understand.

▶ Pray that God will help you to understand the passage and show you how to apply it. Pray for other members in the group too, that they will find the study helpful.

▶ Be willing to take part in the discussions. The leader of the group is not there as an expert with all the answers. They will want everyone to get involved and to share their thoughts and opinions.

▶ However, don't dominate the group! If you are aware that you are saying a lot, make space for others to contribute. Be sensitive to other group members and aim to be encouraging. If you disagree with someone, say so but without putting down their contribution.

FOR INDIVIDUALS

▶ Although this book is written with a group in mind, it can also be easily used by individuals. You obviously won't be able to do the group activities suggested, but you can consider how you would answer the questions and write your thoughts in the space provided.

▶ You may find it helpful to talk to a prayer partner about what you have learnt, and ask them to pray for you as you try and apply what you are learning to your life.

▶ The New International Version of the text is printed in the book. If you use a different version, then read from your own Bible as well.

INTRODUCTION TO BIG THEMES FROM COLOSSIANS

Much of the material in this workbook is based on Spring Harvest's 1998 theme, 'Across the Border Line'. Do you ever feel like you only cross the border line into the world of Christianity once a week, on Sunday, and then on Monday morning cross back into the real world?

Paul was writing to the Colossians to encourage them that their Christian faith did have something to say on the major issues of life, their beliefs could influence their behaviour, and their border crossing into Christianity could be a fantastic journey that lasted a lifetime.

This church, founded by one of Paul's converts, Epaphras, was young and set in a small multi-racial town. Many had accepted the gospel and were showing all the signs of having crossed the border line into faith in Christ. But these new Christians were having trouble growing in their faith, because religious views from outside the church were gaining ground inside it. Paul's response was to remind these young believers of the supremacy of Jesus and to put him first in all things. This was a practical message that affected the everyday issues of work and family; it impacted the church community, and it helped them discern false doctrine. Paul's letter showed that their faith was intensely relevant to their real lives.

Although Paul wrote in a different century and culture, many of the big issues the Colossians were facing are still around today. We still want to know how to be a Christian at work and in the family, how to share our faith with others, and how to keep the church culturally relevant without losing its distinctive message.

If you are ready to tackle some of these big issues, if you want your faith to grow and see it impact every part of your life, then join Paul as he takes us on a journey across the border line.

SALVATION – PASSPORT CONTROL

AIM: to remember how Jesus' death on the cross accomplished our salvation – a unique event with lasting consequences for our lives

We live in a sound-bite culture where many people have their fifteen minutes of fame. Pop stars, actors, politicians, even criminals vie for our attention. But Paul reminds us that Jesus stands above the rest – he alone could reconcile us to God. When we give Jesus the supreme place in our lives we will begin to live out the full life he saved us for and we'll have a faith that makes a difference.

> *He is the image of the invisible God, the firstborn over all creation. For by him all things were created: things in heaven and on earth, visible and invisible, whether thrones or powers or rulers or authorities; all things were created by him and for him. He is before all things, and in him all things hold together. And he is the head of the body, the church; he is the beginning and the firstborn from among the dead, so that in everything he might have the supremacy. For God was pleased to have all his fullness dwell in him, and through him to reconcile to himself all things, whether things on earth or things in heaven, by making peace through his blood, shed on the cross.*
>
> *Once you were alienated from God and were enemies in your minds because of your evil behaviour. But now he has reconciled you by Christ's physical body through death to present you holy in his sight, without blemish and free from accusation – if you continue in your faith, established and firm, not moved from the hope held out in the gospel. This is the gospel that you heard and that has been proclaimed to every creature under heaven, and of which I, Paul, have become a servant.*
>
> *Colossians 1:15–23*

TO SET THE SCENE

Get to know the others in your group by sharing about a significant event or person that has influenced your life. You could play a special piece of music, pass round a picture or any other object that reminds you of that event or person.

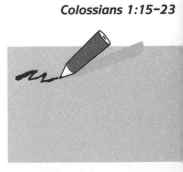

Read Colossians 1:15–23

1. Colossians 1:15–20 is probably an early Christian hymn. Brainstorm together all that it says about Christ – have a scribe write down your answers on a big piece of paper as you go along.

   Firstborn – *In Bible times the eldest son had special rights and privileges. Jesus is called 'firstborn' because he had rights over creation (v15). He is also called firstborn from the dead because he was the first man to rise from the dead with a resurrection body (v18).*

2. In v19 and 22 Jesus is described as a 'reconciler'. What images does this word conjure up in your mind?

3. Paul stresses the reality of Jesus' physical death. Why could we only be reconciled to God through someone dying? Why did it have to be Jesus who died?

4. Many people reject the 'good news.' So how do we explain v20, which says Christ will reconcile 'all things' to himself? Look at 2 Thessalonians 1:8, Romans 3:22, 10:9.

5. Jesus' death on the cross is described in the New Testament in a number of ways:
   ○ As redemption – our freedom being bought at a high price (Rom. 3:24)
   ○ As justification – declared right before God in a court of law (Rom. 3:24)
   ○ As atonement – a sacrifice on our behalf (Rom. 3:25)
   ○ As a demonstration of God's love for us (Rom. 5:8)
   ○ As reconciliation – the restoration of a relationship between us and God (Rom. 5:10)
   ○ As a decisive victory (Col. 2:14–15)

   Which one of these illustrations is most helpful for you to understand what 'salvation' means?

HOW DOES THIS / APPLY TO ME

6. Before we became Christians we were God's enemies (v21). Look at how else Romans 5:6–10 describes us. Share your conversion experience and how your attitudes and actions towards God have changed since you became a Christian. For those who have been brought up in a Christian home, how was v21 true for you?

7. Paul says that we have been reconciled to God (v22) but then adds 'if you continue in your faith' (v23). How can we explain this apparent contradiction?

WHAT DOES / SEARCH / THE BIBLE SAY?

8. How can we explain our salvation in past, present and future terms? (Look at Eph. 2:4–5, 1 Cor. 1:18, Heb. 9:28).

HOW DOES THIS / APPLY TO ME

9. Those who have experienced salvation were once 'aliens' (v21) but are now citizens of 'the kingdom of the Son' (v13–14). How can you live more like citizens of this kingdom where Jesus is supreme? In what practical ways can you show that Jesus is supreme in your life?

WORSHIP

Take the piece of paper that you used for question 1 and put it in the middle of the group. Spend some time praising God for who Jesus is and all that he has done for us. Then in twos pray the prayer in 1:9^b–12 for each other – pray that as you go through the study you will find ways to make Jesus supreme in every area of your life.

DURING THE WEEK

You now hold a passport for the kingdom of God's son. In a passport there is a section for 'distinguishing marks'. As a Christian what would you like your distinguishing mark to be – kindness, hospitality, prayerfulness? Keep your passport in a prominent place this week to remind you to ask God to help you develop these distinguishing marks!

WORLD MISSION – THE FAR COUNTRY

AIM: to consider our part in world mission

God had planned the rescue of humanity before the beginning of the world and had given some clues as to how it might happen. But with the death and resurrection of Jesus, God finally uncovered the mystery. He let people into his secret – Jesus was born to die to take away the sin of the whole world. If we don't get involved in world mission then the mystery of the 'good news' that God has revealed to us is in danger of being hidden from many people.

> *Now I rejoice in what was suffered for you, and I fill up in my flesh what is still lacking in regard to Christ's afflictions, for the sake of his body, which is the church. I have become its servant by the commission God gave me to present to you the word of God in its fullness – the mystery that has been kept hidden for ages and generations, but is now disclosed to the saints. To them God has chosen to make known among the Gentiles the glorious riches of this mystery, which is Christ in you, the hope of glory.*
>
> *We proclaim him, admonishing and teaching everyone with all wisdom, so that we may present everyone perfect in Christ. To this end I labour struggling with all his energy, which so powerfully works in me.*
>
> ***Colossians 1:24–29***

TO SET THE SCENE

Give everyone in the group a newspaper. Find examples of mysteries that have been unravelled – crimes that have been solved, fraudulent business dealings uncovered or new show business romances announced. If your group watches the soaps on TV then list as many of the mysteries that are being unravelled in the plot lines as you can.

Read Colossians 1:24–29

1. Why is it significant that God revealed his 'mystery' to the Gentiles v27?

2. Think about what the phrase 'Christ in you, the hope of glory' means. How could understanding these truths change the lives of those who haven't heard the gospel?

3. Look at what Paul says is involved in proclaiming Jesus. In what kind of ways do modern missionaries fulfil this task?

WHAT DOES
SEARCH
THE BIBLE SAY?

4. Where else in the Bible do you read that God wants everyone to hear the good news? Two thousand years after the mystery was revealed, about one-third of the world's population still haven't heard the good news and many places have no Christian witness at all. There is still much to be done to tell God's mystery of the gospel to the nations.

ENGAGING WITH
THE WORLD

5. How has the world changed in the last fifty years? How are these changes an advantage/disadvantage to the task of spreading the gospel?

HOW DOES THIS
APPLY TO ME

6. How does your lifestyle reflect your interest in spreading God's message across the world?

APPLY THIS TO
MY CHURCH

7. What one action could your church take to speed up the spread of the good news world-wide? What about you?

'Are you ready, if God calls, not only to look out but also to go out? God will be calling some of you reading this to work overseas. I pray that you will hear and respond to his call.'

Stephen Gaukroger

WORSHIP

Paul describes Jesus as glorious riches, a precious jewel. A diamond sparkles because it has many facets. What are the facets or qualities of Jesus that make him like a precious jewel to you? Write these down on a piece of paper. Spend some time worshipping him. On the other side of your paper write down a country or people group that you are interested in. Pray that God's 'mystery' will be revealed to them and they will grow to Christian maturity. If your housegroup leader has a copy of *Operation World* you could find out specific prayer requests for the people or place you're interested in.

FURTHER STUDY

If you want to be more involved in world evangelism as individuals or as a group there are a number of resources which might be helpful.

A good place to start would be:
Operation World, Patrick Johnstone and Jason Mandryk
The Church is Bigger than you Think, Patrick Johnstone

FOR NEXT WEEK

This journey across the border line into Christianity isn't supposed to be a lone trek or a survival special. In fact, the journey will be better the more friends you bring along. Put your answer to question 7 into practice this week – think of the joy that people all across the world will have as they uncover the mystery of the good news.

ACTIVITY PAGE
Adopt a Missionary!

This will require some planning but it will be a fun exercise for the group and an encouragement for the missionary.

Choose a missionary your church supports – if one of the group members has a special link with a missionary that would be a good point of contact. If your church does not support any missionaries personally but gives money to organisations like Operation Mobilisation or Tear Fund, contact the organisation and ask them to link you up with an individual.

Fill a shoebox with treats for your missionary:

▶ A tape recording of your church worship service
▶ A letter written by the group telling about family and church news
▶ Write out the qualities of Christ that make him a special jewel to you on a piece of card with a verse of Scripture or words from a favourite hymn or chorus
▶ Include some goodies that your missionary can't get in the country where they are living. You may need to check with the missionary society about the items you are allowed to send as some gifts may be forbidden.

As a group, pray regularly for your missionary. You could keep up-to-date with their prayer requests via email. Get to know them personally and show them that you care about them and the work that they are doing. Share friendship with them in practical ways – send gifts of money through your church, organise a subscription for a magazine they really enjoy or send regular parcels of special treats.

FALSE TEACHING – THE MINEFIELD

AIM: to be on our guard for false teaching

Someone once said 'If you're going to tell a lie make sure it's a believable one' – the same applies to false teaching. False teaching is rarely so outrageous that everyone recognises it; it is usually subtle, with tinges of truth. Almost imperceptibly the trends and values of secular society sneak into the church. Some are good influences and some are bad, but all need to be evaluated.

See to it that no one takes you captive through hollow and deceptive philosophy, which depends on human tradition and the basic principles of this world rather than on Christ. For in Christ all the fullness of the Deity lives in bodily form, and you have been given fullness in Christ, who is the head over every power and authority.

Therefore do not let anyone judge you by what you eat or drink, or with regard to a religious festival, a New Moon celebration or a Sabbath day. These are a shadow of the things that were to come; the reality, however, is found in Christ. Do not let anyone who delights in false humility and the angels disqualify you for the prize. Such a person goes into great detail about what he has seen, and his unspiritual mind puffs him up with idle notions. He has lost connection with the Head, and from whom the whole body, supported and held together by its ligaments and sinews, grows as God causes it to grow.

Since you died with Christ to the basic principles of this world, why, as though you still belonged to it, do you submit to its rules: "Do not handle! Do not taste! Do not touch!"? These are all destined to perish with use, because they are based on human commands and teachings. Such regulations indeed have an appearance of wisdom, with their self-imposed worship, their false humility and their harsh treatment of the body, but they lack any value in restraining sensual indulgence.

Colossians 2:8–10, 16–23

TO SET THE SCENE

Have three people in your group say three statements about themselves. Two of the statements must be true and one false. The rest of the group need to guess which is the false statement. How easy was it to spot the false statement? What were the clues that gave it away?

Read Colossians 2:8–10, 16–23

1. We don't know exactly what false teaching the Colossians were dealing with. But look at the clues Paul gives us in v8, 16–17, 18–23 to build up a picture of what they were facing.

2. What did Paul say to the Colossians to help them deal with the false teaching? Look at v8–10, 17, 19–20, 23.

3. How does v8 sum up the characteristics of false teaching?

4. Can you think of ways in which the church in the UK has been influenced by false teaching? Think of the ways people have distorted the truth about who Jesus is and also how they have distorted what the Bible says about how we should live as Christians.

5. In the past heretics have been burnt at the stake for bringing error into the church. Now in our more tolerant generation we are reticent to label things wrong. How can we avoid error in what we believe as individuals and as a church? How should we address any errors we see in our church?

6. Sometimes it is good for the church to listen to society and contemporary culture. Brainstorm ways in which the church has rightly been influenced by society in recent years.

7. Not all aspects of our culture have a positive influence on the church. Below are four hallmarks of today's secular culture. For each one, discuss:

○ What danger these influences pose to the church

- How they can be seen in the church already.
- What we can do to prevent them gaining further ground
- Non-rationality – reason is no longer important
- Consumerism – our significance stems from what we own. Having things and freedom of choice are primary values
- Deadening of feelings – our TV culture constantly bombards us with a multiplicity of emotions, which makes it harder for us to feel deeply
- Loss of certainty – we are now suspicious of too much certainty

'Evil is unspectacular and always human, and shares our bed and eats at our own table.'

WH Auden

WORSHIP

The early church wrote creeds to remind Christians of the truths of their faith and also to refute false teaching. Incorporate these creeds into your time of worship.

I believe in God the Father
in Christ his Son
in the Holy Spirit and the remission of sins and life
everlasting through the Holy Church

Cyprian of Carthage

I believe in God the Father almighty
And in Jesus Christ his only Son our Lord
Who was born of the Holy Spirit and the Virgin Mary
Who was crucified under Pontius Pilate and was buried
On the third day he rose again from the dead
Ascended into heaven
Sat at the right hand of the Father
And will come again to judge the living and the dead
And in the Holy Spirit
Holy Church
The remission of sins
The resurrection of the body

Roman Creed – c.200

If you have time, you could write your own statement of faith. Draft some ideas in twos and then share with the group. Take the best ideas from everyone and make a statement of faith that the group agrees with. Use this to declare your beliefs corporately and then allow time for more spontaneous prayers.

FOR NEXT WEEK

False teaching is a minefield! What impact has it had on you? Write down how you have been affected by the issues brought up in question 7. What is the main area where you have unconsciously been relying on false teaching? How can you change this?

FURTHER STUDY

If you would like more information on cults or world religions, three good resources are:

Encyclopaedia of Cults and New Religions, Ankerberg & Weldon
The Truth Twisters, H.J. Berry
The Clash of Worlds, D. Burnett

ACTIVITY PAGE

Jill has started work in your office. She is a Jehovah's Witness. In the course of conversation you find out that the aunt who brought her up was a Christian. Jill has bad memories of her aunt and feels the church they attended was irrelevant and uncaring.
Discuss in twos:
   ○ What would you say to Jill?
   ○ How would you develop the conversation and your friendship with her?
You are on a committee to build a youth club. Of the six other people on the committee, one is Muslim and one Buddhist. At the end of a meeting, someone remarks: 'It is wonderful to have all of these different faiths working together to improve our community. After all, we'll all have to work together in heaven!'
In church someone says to you how dreadful it is you are working with members of other religions. People of other faiths are totally misguided, they say, in fact they are satanic and real Christians should have nothing to do with them.
Discuss in twos:
   ○ How should Christians relate to those of other faiths?
   ○ What would you have said to the people who made these comments?
Share as a group how you would react in these two situations.

> *'It is one thing to show a man is in error, and another to put him in possession of truth.'*
>
> *John Locke*

SPIRITUAL WARFARE – BATTLE ZONE

AIM: to be aware of the spiritual battle that is being waged

Have you ever read the last page of a novel first? You know the outcome of the story but you still have to read the book to discover all the twists and turns of the plot. We know Jesus defeated evil on the cross and one day his victory will be seen for what it is. But in the meantime we are involved in spiritual warfare and we need to be confident of the weapons at our disposal.

> *When you were dead in your sins and in the uncircumcision of your sinful nature, God made you alive with Christ. He forgave us all our sins, having cancelled the written code, with its regulations, that was against us and that stood opposed to us; he took it away, nailing it to the cross. And having disarmed the powers and authorities, he made a public spectacle of them, triumphing over them by the cross.*

> ***Colossians 2:13–15***

TO SET THE SCENE

Spiritual highs are often followed fast by spiritual lows. Remember how the momentous occasion of Jesus' baptism was followed by a period of gruelling temptation in the desert (Mt. 4:1–11). Many times it seems that where God's kingdom is advancing, spiritual opposition intensifies. How have you seen this in your own life and in the life of your church?

WHAT DOES SEARCH THE BIBLE SAY?

1. Spiritual opposition is a difficult concept to define. Look at the range of things it can include for an individual – Acts 13:49–50, 16:16–24, 19:9, Galatians 1:6, 2 Thessalonians 1:4, 2 Timothy 1:15, Titus 1:10.

Read Colossians 2:13–15

These verses explain Jesus' victory over the spiritual forces in military terms. Jesus is portrayed as the triumphant Roman general. He's stripped his enemy of their weapons and is parading them in the street, powerless and disgraced.

2. When we experience spiritual opposition, perhaps a hardship or trial, why are we so slow to remember that Jesus has already defeated the powers of evil?

3. Is Jesus a good role model for how to deal with spiritual opposition? Are there any lessons we can learn from his example? Look at Matthew 4:1–11 and Mark 1:23–28.

4. How else can we defend ourselves personally against Satan's attacks (1 Pet. 5:8–10)?

5. How can we know the difference between spiritual opposition by Satan and barriers or difficulties set in place by God?

ENGAGING WITH

THE WORLD

6. Ephesians 6:12 says 'For our struggle is not against flesh and blood, but against the rulers, against the authorities, against the powers of this dark world and against the spiritual forces of evil in the heavenly realms.' How can we see this spiritual warfare at a national/institutional level?

APPLY THIS TO

MY CHURCH

7. How best can Christians respond collectively to an evil world system? What can your church do?

8. In what ways can Christians give the devil too much or too little credit?

WHAT DOES SEARCH THE BIBLE SAY?

9. Can God use the consequences of spiritual opposition for good? Have a look at Acts 8:1,4; 16:16–34; 1 Peter 1:6–9.

HOW DOES THIS APPLY TO ME

10. Examine your own life – are you aware of Satan's attacks? Have you ignored him too much? What is the weak point he will go for?

WORSHIP

Read Ephesians 6:10–18 again as a group. Allow each person to choose a piece of the armour that they most need to fight in the spiritual battle now. On a large piece of paper draw the 'whole armour of God' with each person drawing in the piece of armour that they most need. Pray in twos for each other that you will use the armour of God in the coming week. Pray for issues of spiritual opposition in your church, families and community.

FOR NEXT WEEK

Across the border line into Christianity is a war zone! Remember to put on the armour of God this week to protect your weak points. Pray this for the others in your group too. Use the sword of the Spirit – memorise a Bible verse to help you withstand the devil's attacks.

notes

FAMILY – VOYAGE OF DISCOVERY

AIM: to reassess how well we are doing at building significant relationships in our church and family

Do you ever feel like you are running just to stand still? All the 'mod cons' that were supposed to speed up tasks so we could have more free time seem to have just given us more time to do more tasks. As the pace of life becomes frantic a key area of our lives is neglected – our relationships.

Therefore, as God's chosen people, holy and dearly loved, clothe yourselves with compassion, kindness, humility, gentleness and patience. Bear with each other and forgive whatever grievances you may have against one another. Forgive as the Lord forgave you. And over all these virtues put on love, which binds them all together in perfect unity.

Let the peace of Christ rule in your hearts, since as members of one body you were called to peace. And be thankful. Let the word of Christ dwell in you richly as you teach and admonish one another with all wisdom, and as you sing psalms, hymns and spiritual songs with gratitude in your hearts to God. And whatever you do, whether in word or deed, do it all in the name of the Lord Jesus, giving thanks to God the Father through him.

Wives, submit to your husbands, as is fitting in the Lord.

Husbands, love your wives and do not be harsh with them.

Children, obey your parents in everything, for this pleases the Lord.

Fathers, do not embitter your children, or they will become discouraged.

Colossians 3:12–21

TO SET THE SCENE

How well do you know your church family? Take turns going around the room, sharing a little known fact about yourself. It doesn't have to be too personal! You could tell the group about a hobby you enjoy, the foreign country where you were brought up, a qualification that you have. How well do you know the other members of the group? Are these types of facts an accurate guide to a person?

Read Colossians 3:12–21

 WHAT DOES **SEARCH** THE BIBLE SAY?

1. We only start treating people differently when we are different ourselves. So how do we 'clothe' ourselves in the Christian virtues? Is it God's work or ours? Look at Galatians 5:22–23 and Romans 6:11–14.

 APPLY THIS TO MY CHURCH

2. God wants the church to be a place of significant relationships where we spur each other on as Christians. To what extent is your church a place where you:
- ○ Bear with each other (v13)
- ○ Forgive one another (v13)
- ○ Teach and advise one another (v16)

Think of all the formal and informal opportunities where these activities may be going on.

 APPLY THIS TO MY CHURCH

3. What else could your church do to encourage these significant relationships to develop?

4. Brainstorm together your top ten tips for effective relationships. These relationships can be church or natural family ones. Our natural family is a place where we need to be building significant and deep relationships. Just because we live with people doesn't mean we know them or are sharing our lives with them!

 HOW DOES THIS APPLY TO ME

5. There has been much debate about the word submit in v18. How do the surrounding verses help you understand what the term means? How does this element of marriage work out in practice for you?

6. Conflict comes into any relationship – whether a
    marriage or a friendship. What advice would you
    give about resolving conflict?

    *'If two people agree on everything... one of
    them is unnecessary.'*
    Ruth Bell Graham

7. Draw a diagram that represents how you feel
    you should prioritise the demands on your time
    – marriage, children, God, church, work, etc.
    Discuss together the various models. How have
    group members juggled these demands and
    maintained their priorities?

8. Imagine the parent of a twelve-year-old child in
    your youth group comes to see you. The child
    has just become a Christian on a weekend away
    with the youth group. The parent thinks the child
    is being brainwashed and doesn't want them to
    attend church any more on Sundays. What would
    you say to the parent and later to the child?

9. How do we 'embitter children' to the point of
    discouragement (v21)? How can we avoid this as
    parents?

HOW DOES THIS APPLY TO ME

10. What our children, spouse, and friends
    most need from us is love and time. Life
    is so full and busy that time is often
    the hardest thing to give them. What
    different choices could you make, what things
    could you delegate, what new attitudes could
    you have in order to make time for the significant
    people in your life?

    *'Unless loving your family is a high priority,
    you may gain the whole world and lose your
    children.'*

    Rob Parsons

WORSHIP
In your time of worship and prayer, if appropriate, share communion together as the body of Christ. Colossians 3:15 reminds us that we are one body called to love and peace. We can only do this because of Christ's love for us demonstrated on the cross and the peace he brought us with God.

FOR NEXT WEEK
Reflect on your own situation – decide to set aside more time this week to spend with someone significant in your life. Plan a date night with your spouse, a trip to McDonalds with your children, a meal out with a friend, or some hours alone with God. Do at least one of these things and put the rest down as dates in your diary!

ACTIVITY PAGE
'Whatever you do, do it all in the name of the Lord Jesus.'

Colossians 3:17

Do everything as Jesus would if he were here – surely this is the key to Christ-likeness. And if we are like Christ we will love others, serve them and give ourselves to them as Jesus would. But in the middle of hectic lives, how can we do things in Jesus' name?

Reflect as a group what doing the following in Jesus' name would mean in practical terms:

- Church ministry
- Relationships with your pastor/minister/church leaders
- Looking after the ones who are sidelined in your church
- Using the time between waking up and leaving for work
- Picking your children up from school
- Looking after your children
- Relating to your work colleagues and your employer

What type of reminders would help you do 'everything in Jesus' name'? A session with your prayer partner? A Bible verse on your fridge or dashboard? A song or picture? Time alone with God each day?

WORLD OF WORK – UNEXPLORED TERRITORY

AIM: to see our work as a mission field, valuable to God

Along with politics and sex, work is almost a taboo subject in our churches. And yet for most of us the workplace is our greatest mission field – it is where we spend most of our time and where we have our greatest sphere of influence.

> *Slaves, obey your earthly masters in everything; and do it, not only when their eye is on you and to win their favour, but with sincerity of heart and reverence for the Lord. Whatever you do, work at it with all your heart, as working for the Lord, not for men, since you know you will receive an inheritance from the Lord as a reward. It is the Lord Christ you are serving. Anyone who does wrong will be repaid for his wrong, and there is no favouritism. Masters, provide your slaves with what is right and fair, because you know that you also have a Master in heaven.*
>
> *Colossians 3:22–4:1*

TO SET THE SCENE

Share with each other what your work is. Describe how you feel about your work.

If your work were a journey would you see it as:
- An uphill climb?
- A ramble?
- An adventure?
- A bumpy road?

If your work were a place to live, would you see it as:
- A four-star hotel?
- A tent?
- A tied cottage?
- A block of flats?

Read Colossians 3:22–4:1

1. How would you define work?

2. Paul is not writing to the Colossians to reject or condone slavery, he's just dealing with their current situation. Brainstorm together what principles you can draw from these verses about the way you do your work.

3. Does doing your work for the Lord and for an inheritance in heaven (v23–24) help you cope with the difficulties of your work situation or does it add more pressure?

4. Why do you think work was part of life before the fall (Gen. 2:15)?

WHAT DOES SEARCH THE BIBLE SAY?

5. The fall made work more difficult (Gen. 3:19) so to what extent can we expect joy and satisfaction in our work? Look at Ecclesiastes 5:18–20.

APPLY THIS TO MY CHURCH

6. In what ways does the church convey the impression that spiritual work is only that done in and for the church?

7. How does 'Whatever you do, work at it with all your heart... . It is the Lord Christ you are serving' (Col. 3:23–24) affect your view of what is spiritual work and what is not?

WHAT DOES SEARCH THE BIBLE SAY?

8. God's heroes in the Bible were workers, fully integrated in to society. Look at the range of jobs that God's servants did:
   ○ Exodus 1:15–20
   ○ Genesis 41:41–45
   ○ Daniel 6:1–3
   ○ 2 Kings 5:1–3
   ○ Acts 16:13–15

   God used these men and women in their place of work to further his plans!

9. Society defines the value of our work in monetary terms. What gives your work particular value to God and value to humanity?

[Handwritten notes in margin:]
conscien
consistent
careful.
honesty.
obedience to authority

midwives.
prime - minister
chief administrator
king   slave girl.
merchant.

compassion.

being open to god.

HOW DOES THIS APPLY TO ME

10. Does witnessing at work only happen when you're sharing the gospel? Give examples of when you have been able to share a biblical perspective at work, whether formally or informally.

WORSHIP

Praise the Lord Jesus for his work of

▶ creation (Col. 1:16)
▶ sustaining creation (Col. 1:17)
▶ redemption (Col. 1:21–22)

Then put an object that represents your work in the middle of the group. It could be a calculator, a piece of chalk, or a pair of washing up gloves; anything that is symbolic of your work. As each person presents their object, pray that they will see their work as their worship to God and do it in his name. Share work-related issues that people are concerned about for the coming week. Pray that we will bring justice, truth, and love to our workplaces.

DURING THE WEEK

You are now entering the mission field! This week, see your work as your ministry for God. It is where God has placed you so that you grow spiritually, serve him faithfully, and share him with others.

FOR FURTHER STUDY

If you want to discuss the topic of work further contact the London Institute for Contemporary Christianity on 0207 3999 555 or www.licc.org.uk. They have various resources available and will be able to put you in contact with other organisations.

To give you a taster, you could try Mark Greene's book *Thank God it's Monday* (SU) or David Oliver's *Work – Prison or Place of Destiny?* (Word).

AT WORK TOGETHER

Spring Harvest runs a conference dealing with workplace issues. Contact the Spring Harvest office for details:

t.   01825 769111
e.   info@springharvest.org
w. www.springharvest.org

ACTIVITY PAGE

Many churches hold missionary conferences or missionary weekends, where they pray and learn about God's work world-wide. Why not ask your church leaders if you could organise a missionary weekend with a difference?

We spend time praying for missionaries overseas, which is good. But we are all missionaries – each of us, whether we are a homemaker, business executive or shop worker, has a mission field of people we can influence for Christ.

Organise a missionary day for your church. Here are some suggestions to help you get started:

▶ Get people to bring a packed lunch, as they would to work
▶ Have speakers from different fields of work explaining how they have brought a Christian perspective to their workplace
▶ Have seminars to discuss together how to tackle ethical issues in the workplace, such as sexism, racism, financial misconduct
▶ Have speakers to address issues that the church rarely hears about – ambition and promotion in the workplace, the value of homemakers in God's economy
▶ Get people of the same profession or field of work into groups to discuss issues of particular relevance to them. These could become regular prayer groups
▶ Make missionary prayer cards for each member of the church. On the card indicate the person's name, display a photo and describe their vocation. Let members share prayer cards with different people in the church. Contact each other via email to keep up-to-date with work-related prayer requests.

EVANGELISM – TRAVELLERS TALES

 AIM: to focus on making the most of the opportunities for evangelism that God gives us

Sharing the gospel is often an embarrassing experience both for the Christian and the unbeliever. Here Paul gives us some practical tips to make evangelism a natural part of who we are and what we do.

> *Devote yourselves to prayer, being watchful and thankful. And pray for us, too, that God may open a door for our message, so that we may proclaim the mystery of Christ, for which I am in chains. Pray that I may proclaim it clearly, as I should. Be wise in the way you act towards outsiders; make the most of every opportunity. Let your conversation be always full of grace, seasoned with salt, so that you may know how to answer everyone.*

Colossians 4:2–6

TO SET THE SCENE
You have already shared together how you became Christians. Spend some time now focusing on the particular event, person, verse of the Bible or thought that made you cross the border line and trust Christ as your Saviour. Are there any patterns emerging?

1.   Share with each other any recent evangelistic conversations you have had.

Read Colossians 4:2–6

Be wise: we are to be wise in the way we speak to and behave towards outsiders. This means understanding where they are coming from. Modern society has been described as:

- post-Christian
  - a growing ignorance of the Bible and the truth about Jesus
- postmodern
  - there are no certainties of life, only a range of choices. You know the truth for you through experience
- fragmented
  - society is made of many sub-groups like commuters, career women, bikers

ENGAGING WITH THE WORLD

2. Take each of these descriptions. How does it affect how you would explain the gospel?

3. How do these descriptions alter the type of evangelistic events your church should put on?

HOW DOES THIS APPLY TO ME

4. Colossians 4:5 says 'Make the most of every opportunity'. What opportunities could you take to express the truth about Jesus in a relevant way? What stops you?

APPLY THIS TO MY CHURCH

5. What opportunities are there in your community to live out the gospel? How could you be making the most of them?

WHAT DOES SEARCH THE BIBLE SAY?

6. Look at these examples of evangelistic conversations in the Bible:

- ○ John 4:1–26
- ○ John 3:1–21
- ○ Acts 8:26–40
- ○ Acts 17:16–34

Evangelistic preaching is vital. But from these verses what are some of the advantages of evangelistic conversations?

APPLY THIS TO MY CHURCH

7. Most people become Christian when they are in regular conversation with Christians, and even involved in church life. What else can your church do to make sure it is not just a place for those who are already saved?

8. Our conversations are to be 'full of grace and seasoned with salt'. How can we demonstrate graciousness when sharing the gospel?

9. Sometimes our conversation with outsiders is boring and unIntelligible to them. Think of creative ways, using picture language, to describe the Christian concepts of:
   ○ salvation
   ○ sin
   ○ redemption

10. Paul wants us to know how to answer people's questions about our faith. What do you think are the top ten questions non-Christians have about Christianity?

11. In twos, choose a question from your top ten list and discuss how best to answer it. Come back together and pool all your ideas.

WORSHIP
Pray for each other to be salt and light in the community this coming week. Light some candles to remind you that just as Jesus is the light of the world, so we are to be light in our communities. Have a bowl of salt and take some of the grains in your hand, remembering we are to be seasoning.

FURTHER STUDY
There are lots of books to help you answer the questions people ask about Christianity. Here are some to start you off:

Basic Christianity – John Stott
Answers to Tough Questions – Josh McDowell
Searching Issues – Nicky Gumbel

FOR NEXT WEEK
Pray that God would give you an opportunity to share the gospel. Be on the lookout for the opportunities he is giving you and don't be reluctant to take them!

PRESSING ON – THE FINAL FRONTIER

AIM

AIM: to remind us of the need to finish the Christian life well

Once you have crossed the border line into the Kingdom of God the journey is not always easy. At times the terrain is difficult. Paul encourages us here to persevere because the final frontier into the kingdom of heaven is in sight.

Tychicus will tell you all the news about me. He is a dear brother, a faithful minister and fellow servant in the Lord. I am sending him to you for the express purpose that you may know about our circumstances and that he may encourage your hearts. He is coming with Onesimus, our faithful and dear brother, who is one of you. They will tell you everything that is happening here.

My fellow prisoner Aristarchus sends you his greetings, as does Mark, the cousin of Barnabas. (You have received instructions about him; if he comes to you, welcome him.) Jesus, who is called Justus, also sends greetings. These are the only Jews among my fellow workers for the kingdom of God, and they have proved a comfort to me. Epaphras, who is one of you and a servant of Christ Jesus, sends greetings. He is always wrestling in prayer for you, that you may stand firm in the will of God, mature and fully assured. I vouch for him that he is working hard for you and for those at Laodicea and Hierapolis. Our dear friend Luke, the doctor, and Demas send greetings. Give my greetings to the brothers at Laodicea, and to Nympha and the church in her house.

After this letter has been read to you, see that it is also read in the church of the Laodiceans and that you in turn read the letter from Laodicea.

Tell Archippus: 'See to it that you complete the work you have received in the Lord.'

I, Paul, write this greeting in my own hand. Remember my chains. Grace be with you.

Colossians 4:7–18

TO SET THE SCENE

Look at the diagrams portraying spiritual growth over time. Which graph best represents your Christian life? What circumstances have encouraged you to grow most in spiritual terms?

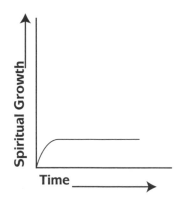

Read Colossians 4:7–18

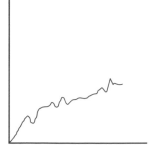

1. Pick out the words or phrases from these verses that tell us Paul's fellow workers were persevering as Christians; they were aiming to finish well.

2. Colossians 4:17 mentions Archippus. We also hear about him in Philemon, verse 2. What does Paul say about him in his letter to Philemon? What picture do you get of him?

3. Paul encourages Archippus to complete the work he 'received in the Lord'. Get into two groups and brainstorm: What are the clues that what we are doing is:
   ○ The Lord's work (done for him and in his strength)?
   ○ Our work (done for us and in our strength)?

4. There are lots of jobs to be done in the church – all could be called 'the Lord's work'. Look at the following list – how we can know which particular job God wants us to do?

○ Hoovering the church and setting the chairs out each Sunday because it is a job that just needs to be done.

○ The Pastor makes a final plea for Sunday school teachers for the 11–13-year-olds – otherwise the group will have to be disbanded.

○ You're gifted and experienced in working with old people and your church hasn't got a ministry in this area. Should you start one?

5. Paul encourages Archippus to persist in the work of the Lord. Look at the following passages to remind yourself of the areas God wants us to persevere in:

○ Ephesians 6:18
○ Romans 12:11
○ 2 Corinthians 8:10–11
○ 2 Corinthians 11:23–28

6. What are the things that make it difficult to persevere in God's work? What makes you want to quit?

7. What can we do as individuals and as a church to help each other persevere?

8. Perseverance isn't something we should avoid or begrudge, because God says it has a positive benefit for us. What is the value of perseverance?

Look at:
○ Romans 5:3–5
○ 2 Peter 1:5–8
○ James 1:2–4

9. Share together examples from your own life where perseverance and struggles have helped you develop Christian character qualities.

HOW DOES THIS APPLY TO ME

10. Paul's main aim in writing to the Colossians was to remind them that Jesus Christ was completely supreme and utterly sufficient. In what areas do you need to recognise this so that you can keep on persevering?

WORSHIP

Write a letter to God (see below). If you are able, share with the group what you wrote. What has been the most interesting thing you have learnt doing this workbook? What is the most important thing God has taught you? Spend some time in silence, recommitting yourself to God in these particular areas. Praise God that he is not going to give up on you – he will give you the strength to persevere. Pray for each other, committing each other to God for the rest of the journey across the border line.

FOR FUTURE WEEKS

Keep the letter you wrote to God (see Activity Page) in your Bible. Open it again only when you need to remind yourself of the promises you made to God and he made to you. Pray through the Bible verses that you chose to help you persevere. Contact another member of the group and arrange to meet up to pray together.

> 'He who began a good work in you will carry it on to completion until the day of Christ Jesus.'
>
> **Philippians 1:6**

ACTIVITY PAGE

Write a letter to God about the high points of this Bible study series for you.
- What interesting things have you learnt?
- What is the most important thing God has taught you?
- What decisions do you need to make in response?
- Are there any other areas you need to grow in?
- Write down some Bible verses to help you persevere through the difficult times, which will come
- Some helpful verses might be:
  Revelation 3:5–6, 21–22
  Hebrews 12:1–3
  James 1:2–4

Seal your letter. Only open it when you need to remind yourself of the commitments you made to God and he makes to you.

LEADERS' GUIDE

TO HELP YOU LEAD

You may have led a housegroup many times before or this may be your first time. Here is some advice on how to lead these studies:

▶ As a group leader, you don't have to be an expert or a lecturer. You are there to facilitate the learning of the group members – helping them to discover for themselves the wisdom in God's word. You should not be doing most of the talking or dishing out the answers, whatever the group expects from you!

▶ You do need to be aware of the group's dynamics, however. People can be quite quick to label themselves and each other in a group situation. One person might be seen as the expert, another the moaner who always has something to complain about. One person may be labelled as quiet and not be expected to contribute, another person may always jump in with something to say. Be aware of the different type of individuals in the group, but don't allow the labels to stick. You may need to encourage those who find it hard to get a word in, and quieten down those who always have something to say. Talk to members between sessions to find out how they feel about the group.

▶ The sessions are planned to try and engage every member in active learning. Of course you cannot force anyone to take part if they don't want to, but it won't be too easy to be a spectator. Activities that ask everyone to write down a word, or talk in twos, and then report back to the group are there for a reason. They give everyone space to think and form their opinion, even if not everyone voices it out loud.

▶ Do adapt the sessions for your group as you feel is appropriate. Some groups may know each other very well and will be prepared to talk at a deep level. New groups may take a bit of time to get to know each other before making themselves vulnerable, but encourage members to share their lives with each other.

▶ Encourage a number of replies to each question. The study is not about finding a single right answer, but about sharing experiences and thoughts in order to find out how to apply the Bible to people's lives. When brainstorming, don't be too quick to evaluate the contributions. Write everything down and then have a look to see which suggestions are worth keeping.

www.springharvest.org/workbooks/

▶ Similarly encourage everyone to ask questions, to voice doubts and to discuss difficulties. Some parts of the Bible are difficult to understand. Sometimes the Christian faith throws up paradoxes. Painful things happen to us that make it difficult to see what God is doing. A housegroup should be a safe place to express all of this. If discussion doesn't resolve the issue, send everyone away to pray about it between sessions, and ask your minister for advice.

▶ Give yourself time in the week to read through the Bible passage and the questions. Read the Leaders' notes for the session, as different ways of presenting the questions are sometimes suggested. However, during the session don't be too quick to come in with the answer – sometimes people need space to think.

▶ Delegate as much as you like! The easiest activities to delegate are reading the text, and the worship sessions, but there are other ways to involve the group members. Giving people responsibility can help them own the session much more.

▶ Pray for group members by name, that God would meet with them during the week. Pray for the group session, for a constructive and helpful time. Ask the Lord to equip you as you lead the group.

THE STRUCTURE OF EACH SESSION

Feedback: find out what people remember from the previous session, or if they have been able to act during the week on what was discussed last time.

To set the scene: an activity or a question to get everyone thinking about the subject to be studied.

Bible reading: it's important to actually read the passage you are studying during the session. Ask someone to prepare this in advance or go around the group reading a verse or two each. Don't assume everyone will be happy to read out loud.

Questions and activities: adapt these as appropriate to your group. Some groups may enjoy a more activity-based approach, some may prefer just to discuss the questions. Try out some new things!

Worship: suggestions for creative worship and prayer are included, which give everyone an opportunity to respond to God, largely individually. Use these alongside singing or other group expressions of worship. Add a prayer time with opportunities to pray for group members and their families and friends.

For next week: this gives a specific task to do during the week, helping people to continue to think about or apply what they have learned.

For further study: suggestions are given for those people who want to study the themes further. These could be included in the housegroup if you feel it's appropriate and if there is time.

WHAT YOU NEED

A list of materials that are needed is printed at the start of each session in the Leaders' Guide. In addition you will probably need:

Bibles: the main Bible passage is printed in each session so that all the members can work from the same version. It will be useful to have other Bibles available, or to ask everyone to bring their own, so that other passages can be referred to.

Paper and pens: for people who need more space than is in the book!

Flip chart: it is helpful to write down people's comments during a brainstorming session, so that none of the suggestions is lost. There may not be space for a proper flip chart in the average lounge, and having one may make it feel too much like a business meeting or lecture. Try getting someone to write on a big sheet of paper on the floor or coffee table, and then stick this up on the wall with blu-tack.

GROUND RULES

How do people know what is expected of them in a housegroup situation? Is it ever discussed, or do we just pick up clues for each other? You may find it helpful to discuss some ground rules for the housegroup at the start of this course, even if your group has been going a long time. This also gives you an opportunity to talk about how you, as the leader, see the group. Ask everyone to think about what they want to get out of the course. How do they want the group to work? What values do they want to be part of the group's experience; honesty, respect, confidentiality? How do they want their contributions to be treated? You could ask everyone to write down three ground rules on slips of paper and put them in a bowl. Pass the bowl around the group. Each person takes out a rule and reads it, and someone collates the list. Discuss the ground rules that have been suggested and come up with a top five. This method enables everyone to contribute fairly anonymously. Alternatively, if your group are all quite vocal, have a straight discussion about it!

ICONS

AIM

The aim of the session

ENGAGING WITH

THE WORLD

Engaging with the world

WHAT DOES

SEARCH

THE BIBLE SAY?

Investigate what else the Bible says

HOW DOES THIS

APPLY TO ME

How does this apply to me?

APPLY THIS TO

MY CHURCH

What about our church?

NB not all questions in each session are covered, some are self-explanatory

SESSION 1

MATERIALS NEEDED

▶ Music, pictures, or objects that remind group members of an event or person that has had a major influence on them

▶ Music system if needed by a member of the group

TO SET SCENE

Contact the group members in advance and tell them about this activity. Ask them to think about an event or person that has had a significant influence on their lives. Encourage them to bring an object, picture or music that reminds them of this person or event.

Give time for people to share together – perhaps work in twos or threes if you have a large housegroup. This exercise should be a good icebreaker for the group as they begin to build relationships with each other. It will also be a reminder how we are influenced and shaped by so many things – our aim should be that Jesus is the chief influence in our lives.

1. He is the exact representation (image) of God so reveals God to us; he is supreme over all creation (v15). He created everything for himself (v16). He is eternal and sustains the world and everything in it (v17). He is the head of the church; he was the first to rise from the dead with a resurrection body and is proof we too will rise (v18). He has always been supreme over all things but his resurrection showed this to men (v18). He is fully God (v19). His death is the means by which humans can have peace with God and also harmony be restored to creation (v20).

2. A reconciler is someone who will bring two estranged parties together. It is someone outside of the two warring parties, just as it was Jesus who brought God and man together.

3. In Romans 6:23 and throughout the Old Testament sacrificial system we see that sin had to be paid for by blood – that was God's requirement. We deserved to die for our own sins; no one else could die in our place because they would be paying for their own sins, not ours. Only Jesus could die for the sins of the world: because he was sinless, he could take on the sins of other people.

4. Jesus' death on the cross is sufficient for all people to be saved but they have to respond in obedience, faith and belief. Reconciliation will be fully realised with the new heavens and the new earth – everyone will acknowledge Jesus as Lord and the effects of sin on creation will be overturned.

6. Romans 5 describes us as powerless (v6), ungodly (v6), sinners (v8), enemies (v10). Even in Christian homes when behaviour may look godly, we can still be enemies of God in our minds by not honouring him in our attitudes.

7. When we become Christians we are reconciled to God but this is only the beginning of our relationship with him. God knows genuine faith will continue to the end, but we find out whether faith is genuine only if we continue to the end.

8. In the past when we first came to Christ our sins were forgiven, their penalty paid for (Eph. 2:4–5). In the present, we are being made more like Christ by sanctification (1 Cor. 1:18). In the future, the presence of sin will be totally removed and we will be like Christ (Heb. 9:28).

9. Encourage people to give varied and practical answers.

WORSHIP
Perhaps you could play a CD to begin your time of praise together.

DURING THE WEEK
Remind people that next week you will begin by asking them how their distinguishing marks are developing!

SESSION 2

MATERIALS NEEDED
▶ Newspapers from the previous week
▶ *Operation World*, Patrick Johnstone and Jason Mandryk, if you have a copy.

FEEDBACK
Have a quick recap of last week and see how people's distinguishing marks are developing!

TO SET THE SCENE
Give newspapers out to your group. Set a time limit on people looking for mysteries that have been solved and have a scribe write down everyone's findings. We find satisfaction in solving a mystery. We appreciate knowing the truth and being presented with the facts – think about those who haven't had the opportunity to hear the mystery of the gospel.

1. Salvation is now available for non-Jews – it is universal. God offers reconciliation to all the world. Look at Ephesians 2:11–22 if you want to investigate this issue further.
2. Believers are indwelt by the Holy Spirit and his life within us is the proof that we will be in heaven with God, we will have resurrection bodies (Col. 3:4, 2 Thes. 2:14). For unbelievers this 'mystery' offers them peace with God, hope and a purpose for the future, power to live to please God – encourage your group to come up with as many answers as possible.
3. Paul worked hard – he taught people and sometimes had to warn them. His goal was not just converts but disciples. Growing people to Christian maturity involves sharing our lives with them, it means not just teaching them about God but how his word applies to their lives, it means getting to know them well enough that we can gently correct them. Modern missionaries do this via radio, as tentmakers, working alongside nationals, etc.
4. There are many examples your group could give. To start you off:
   ○ Jesus said 'Go into all the world... to make disciples' (Mt. 28:19–20)
   ○ Peter realised the gospel was for the gentiles and not just the Jews when he was at Cornelius' house (Acts 10:34–43)
   ○ Simeon realised Gentiles were included in God's plan (Lk. 2:30–32)
5. The world has become a smaller place, communication and technology have improved – this has enabled the spread of the gospel through radio; increased Bible production; improved travel to far away destinations. But the growth of cities has brought more secularism and materialism, so people don't know or

feel they need God. The number of countries closed to the gospel has also increased.

6. We may need to make changes to our lifestyle to reflect Christianity's world-wide appeal. Try crossing the social and cultural boundaries where you live; make friends with people of different nationalities; live more simply in order to give money to missions. Show concern for the world that God wants us to reach by being involved in moral and political issues, avoiding waste, avoiding products made by damaging other people.

SESSION 3

FEEDBACK

If people are willing to share, ask them what one action they have chosen to speed up the task of world missions. Encourage people to write down in a journal all the discoveries and decisions they make during this series, as there is a lot to take in. It would be good to revisit these topics and get a progress report at a later date.

TO SET THE SCENE

This activity will help the group get to know each other better. Hopefully it should demonstrate that errors are not always easy to spot. The most successful false teaching is subtle and quite believable!

1. The false teachers seemed to be teaching: reliance on human wisdom and the traditional teaching of the Greeks v8; to rely on ceremonialism v16–17; that extra secret knowledge could be obtained by the super-spiritual v18; angels were objects of worship v18; to rely on rules and regulation v20–23.

2. Paul reminded the Colossians that Christ was fully God and that they were complete in Christ v8–10. They did not need anything extra, only to rely on Christ and to live out the reality that they had a new lifestyle as Christians v17, 19–20. Furthermore, this false teaching had no power to restrain sin v23.

3. False teaching is a trap; it sounds sophisticated but really is a sham. It is man-made and based on worldly principles.

4. Errors about Jesus: that he was not divine; that his cross wasn't enough for salvation, instead we need to earn it. Errors about the Christian life: God will heal all Christians if they have enough faith; God will materially prosper his followers; Christians must follow rules and regulations like Old Testament Jews to please God.

5. a) Personal Bible reading and systematic Bible teaching in the church; teaching about the cults and other religions; looking carefully at our church practices in the light of Scripture on a regular basis.

    b) If you think there is false teaching going on, look carefully about what the Bible teaches on the matter, read what expert theologians have to say, talk to your minister or elders, stay humble and be willing to be shown where you may be wrong, don't seek a following for your own point of view.

6. Encourage the group to give as many suggestions as possible: for example – the treatment of slaves, organisational structures, being more aware of caring for the environment.

7. Non-rationality – sometimes the church emphasizes feelings and emotions over the word of God. We need to keep a balance. Discipleship requires our minds to be engaged (Rom. 12:1, Eph. 4:23, Col. 3:10),

Consumerism – sometimes we treat church like a supermarket, we go to the church where we get what we want; we expect a return from our investment. People are accepted in our churches because of what they own, and what they can bring to the church. We need to get back to a proper perspective of who we are before God and remember that all we are is because of him.

Deadening of feelings – we are so used to being bombarded emotionally, we can try to do the same thing in our worship services. We need to give people time and space for God to touch them.

Loss of certainty – we react either by holding on to beliefs dogmatically when there is room for us to be humble or we doubt when there is no reason to. We need to teach the truths of Christianity, discuss the debatable issues, and pray that God will touch people's hearts, so belief is not just academic.

SESSION 4

MATERIALS

▶ A large piece of paper for the worship session

FEEDBACK

Ask if anyone discovered one of the mines of false teaching in their own lives. If they did, how did they manage to remove it before it became dangerous? Observe everyone's right to privacy but encourage them to keep thinking about these issues.

TO SET THE SCENE

Sometimes our spiritual lows come when we've stopped depending on God, other times they come when Satan uses our sinfulness for his purposes, and sometimes opposition comes from outside. Whatever the reason, spiritual lows remind us we are in a war zone and Satan doesn't like us gaining any ground.

1. Spiritual opposition can be blatant – an evil spirit in someone – or it can be behind human opposition, resulting in persecution, hardships such as prison, people refusing to believe, people deserting Christ, trials, being deserted, and false teachers influencing the church.

2. We forget we're in a war situation and rarely see our difficulties in terms of spiritual opposition. Perhaps we're too independent and like to deal with our problems ourselves.

3. Jesus quoted the Bible to the devil. Mark 1:23–28 isn't prescriptive for every Christian but it does show us that Jesus wasn't fearful of evil spirits and he didn't confront them with showmanship. If mature Christians do seek to remove demons they must do so carefully and with faith in Jesus' name and power (Acts 16:16–18).

4. Being self-controlled and alert. Standing firm in the faith. Don't feel you are unique – other Christians are facing enemy attacks. Remember God will give you grace, he will restore you and help you resist. Look forward to heaven where your place is secure.

5. Sometimes the Holy Spirit makes us aware of who is causing the barrier; sometimes we will never know; sometimes we find out in retrospect and other

times we need to persevere in pushing the doors until the way forward becomes clear.

6. We can see spiritual forces in operation at an institutional level in the bias towards racism, sexism, exploitation of the weak, love of power and self-interest. The Nazi regime is an extreme example.

7. We shouldn't run away or just sit around waiting for Jesus to return – we need to act together as a body. We should pray and take righteous action where possible. Get the group to think of issues on which they could act today. Remember that the systems are the enemy, not the people in them.

8. We give Satan too much credit by speculating about him endlessly, seeing him everywhere, seeing a demon possession every time there is sinful behaviour, and accusing him of every hardship we face. We give Satan too little credit if we cynically dismiss him as a primitive superstition.

9. Yes. For example, God used the persecution of the church to spread the gospel and trials to refine faith. It is up to us to see spiritual opposition as an opportunity for spiritual growth and for God to fulfil his purposes world-wide.

SESSION 5

MATERIALS
▶ Slips of paper and a bowl for the 'To set the scene' exercise
▶ Bread and wine for the communion, if using

TO SET THE SCENE
Use this exercise to discuss how well you know each other. Are you really sharing each others' lives or do you only know each other superficially?

1. Part of 'clothing' ourselves is a decision of our will. Another part is God producing these qualities in us by the Holy Spirit as we daily yield to him. It is a both/and process.

2. Think about the informal and formal ways these aspects go on in your church – preaching, mentoring younger Christians, providing meals for those in need, in relationships with each other, in songs and hymns.

3. There are various ideas to promote significant relationships: one-to-one Bible studies, accountability groups, discipleship groups, fellowship lunches, etc.

4. Ideas such as: good communication, listening to each other, expressing love often, not returning to old ground in an argument, saying sorry, being aware of your own failings, spending time together, accepting the other person's faults.

5. From v18: submission can't be demanded, only willingly given. It does not lessen a woman's value and dignity because it is something 'fitting in the Lord'. It is given in the context of a husband loving a wife as Christ loved the church. Paul has already mentioned forgiveness and other Christian characteristics, and while submission is not dependent upon these it can most easily be expressed in this context.

6. Never attack the person's character, stick to the issue you're dealing with, don't revert to past hurts or concerns, and say sorry if you are wrong.

7. People could have many ways of expressing their ideas. Discuss the fact that God should always be our number one priority, affecting every other area of our lives. Our other priorities may change in the different seasons of life.

8. Discuss issues such as: the child honouring their parents may win the parent round; the child should obey God when God's laws are at stake (Acts 5:29). Would there be any way you could handle the situation so that both the child and parent are satisfied? Would it help to invite the parent along to see what happens in church?

9. We can avoid embittering our children by setting reasonable boundaries and sticking to them, being fair with discipline, spending time with them in fun as well as teaching them our values, demonstrating our faith by our lives.

10. People could make many decisions on this issue. Recognise we all have a choice in the way that we spend our time, we can re-establish our priorities, we need to decide to carve out time for those that matter to us today.

WORSHIP
In some cases, it might be appropriate to mention to your minister about your wish to share communion together as a group. Adapt this section to your church setting.

SESSION 6

MATERIALS
▶ Objects that represent people's work for the worship session

FEEDBACK
People could report back on how they managed to spend more time with family, friends and God. How did the date-night go? Did spending more time with your children make a difference to family life? What did you have to miss in order to spend more time with God – was it worth it?

TO SET THE SCENE
Encourage people to share what they do. Be sensitive to some who may feel embarrassed about what they do in comparison with the other members of the group. Affirm everyone.

1. It is all the tasks we do. It is where we use our gifts and resources; it is how we contribute to humanity. Work is not work just because we get paid for it.

2. We do tasks to the best of our ability whether we are supervised or not, not to win favour or preferential treatment. We do our work wholeheartedly because ultimately our boss is God. Our reward will come in heaven, so we should be focused and conscientious.

3. It depends how you look at it. We will receive a reward in heaven if we have worked well but equally we will be answerable for lack of effort and wrong attitudes.

4. Genesis shows us God worked, he was creative and orderly. We are made in his image so we are workers too.

5. Because of the fall, work will not be a source of unbridled joy and satisfaction. But there will be elements of these things – when we've accomplished tasks, helped people, met goals, etc. Being able to enjoy these pleasures is God's gift to us.

6. Churches rarely talk of ministry as being what you do at work – we don't pray, talk about or preach about work very much. We pray for people when they lead the Sunday school but rarely for what they do the rest of the week. A person's spirituality is often still judged by how many meetings they attend.

7. Our relationship with Christ should have an impact on all that we do – whether it is in the church, with our children, in the marketplace, in the workplace, wherever we are. It should help us see our lives as an integrated whole. God is interested in us serving him with every part of our lives – he wants us to live passionately for him

8. God used midwives, prime minister Joseph, administrator Daniel, a servant girl and a merchant. God used the professions of these people and the influence they had, because of their work, directly to affect the course of history.

9. Whatever people's work is, it is of value to God: regardless of the evangelistic opportunities, because we do it for him, in his strength and for his glory. Our work is of value to humanity because it maintains the order in our society and at some point brings benefit to it. Some of our work may bring a redemptive element, such as justice or hope.

10. Encourage people to see that witnessing isn't only sharing the gospel verbally. We are witnesses at work because Christ is working in us (2 Cor. 5:17); because we work in his strength; because we offer a biblical perspective, without even mentioning the Bible, on personal, general and work-related issues. Perhaps your group can recall incidents when this informal witnessing occurred.

WORSHIP

Contact people in advance and ask them to bring an object that represents their work. Having an object will help focus people's minds – as they use that object in the coming week they will remember in a fresh way that their work is God's work too.

SESSION 7

MATERIALS
▶ Matches, candles, a bowl of salt

FEEDBACK
Report back how your working week has been. Remember to ask the group how any specific issues they prayed for have turned out.

TO SET THE SCENE
This is not intended to embarrass anyone but to highlight the many elements and people that are involved in each person's conversion. Emphasise the different ways that God uses to save each of us.

1. This question is not to make you feel guilty; some people are more natural evangelists than others. Perhaps it may show that people understand less of the Christian faith than in previous years so our conversations need to go right back to the basics.

2. We can't assume people have any previous knowledge of Christianity or that there is any inherent belief in Jesus. People will have difficulty with the exclusivity of Christianity. Perhaps we can show them that it is possible to find certainty and meaning in life.

3. We need to show that Christianity is experientially true by demonstrating it in our lives, by sharing our lives with others. It would be good to aim our evangelistic events at certain groups, and to restore community life through love.

4. Encourage people to be open about their fears and to take even the small opportunities that present themselves.

5. Some ideas are – prison ministry, getting involved in local festivals, being a school governor, teacher's assistant, hosting seminars on stress management or parenting classes.

6. Taking time to have conversations with individuals shows that we care for them. Conversations force us to listen to people, deal with their doubts and personal questions. They make us relate to everyday life and situations, and they give the other person opportunity to respond.

7. Avoid Christian clichés, welcome people, tell them the page number for the Bible reading, have bridge-builder events where they are involved.

8. Show care for the individual, respect them by listening, don't view them as evangelism fodder but have a future interest in them. Don't be obsessed about winning the argument.

9. Use pictures to draw your ideas down if it helps – be creative!

10. Common questions are – why does God allow suffering? What about the people who have never heard the gospel? What about other religions? How can a God of love send people to hell? Hasn't science disproved Christianity?

11. Pool resources and discuss the issues so that the group feels more equipped to tackle them in future.

SESSION 8

MATERIALS
▌ Notepaper and envelopes for letters to God

FEEDBACK
Share any exciting evangelistic conversations members of the group had last week. Take time to pray for the individuals and situations involved.

TO SET THE SCENE
When have you grown the most as a Christian? What effect have struggles and having to persevere made on your Christian growth? Often we can see in retrospect that we have grown more spiritually in difficult times. Perhaps difficult circumstances force us to trust God more.

1. Verses 7 and 9: Paul's companions are called 'faithful'. Epaphras is always praying (v12) and working hard for the Christians (v13).

2. He is a fellow soldier – so he is sharing in the gospel work of preaching and teaching as Timothy did (2 Tim. 3).

3. God's work is centred on Christ and his kingdom, it is done by the power of Holy Spirit, for his glory. Doing our own work is driven by ambition and feeding our egos, we're reluctant to share it with others, we want all the glory, and we're not interested in any new thing God may want to do.

4. There are jobs in the church that just have to be done to make the church function – a bit like putting out the rubbish at home. We all play a part in them. But it is also important to find out what our spiritual gifts are – if we minister out of guilt rather than a passion, we'll soon feel like giving up.

5. Paul encourages us to persevere in prayer, serving, giving financially, giving ourselves and caring for each other,

6. We can get physically weary and tired by facing the same challenges. At times we face opposition – from people, circumstances and from the spiritual realm. We can be distracted and feel like giving up when we don't receive any encouragement.

7. As individuals we should take care of our bodies with a healthy lifestyle; pray; look to the example of Christ who finished well (Jn. 5:36, 19:30) and remember God's promise to be with us through the Holy Spirit (Mt. 28:20). As a church, we should encourage each other; affirm the ministry of others; and remember that we only persevere for a while because Christ is returning.

8. Perseverance produces character qualities that make us more like Jesus.

9. Often we can see in retrospect that difficulties are opportunities for us to grow spiritually. Perhaps realising this will help us accept difficulties in the future. We can ask God to use the circumstances of life and any struggles we may face to make us more like Jesus.

WORSHIP
As this is the last session of the series allow people more time for prayer. Give people the opportunity to reflect and to make their commitments to God.

SPRING HARVEST BIBLE STUDIES
BIG THEMES FROM COLOSSIANS

Quantity discount offer

To buy quantities of this workbook at a discount for use in study groups, please use the voucher below.

Get **Free** copies

- -

Name of Church representative: _____

Dear Retailer,
This completed voucher entitles the bearer to free additional copies of Spring Harvest Bible Workbooks. Please indicate the number of free copies supplied.

item	✔	cost
Buy 10 copies, get **1 free** (11 copies total)		£29.90
Buy 25 copies, get **5 free** (30 copies total)		£74.75
Buy 50 copies, get **15 free** (65 copies total)		£149.50

Vouchers will be credited less normal discount. Please return completed voucher to STL Customer Services, PO Box 300, Carlisle, CA3 0QS, by 31/01/2003

Name of Retailer: _____

STL A/C No: _____

Only one voucher to be used per customer. Voucher cannot be used in conjunction with any other offer. Voucher cannot be exchanged for anything other than the above product. No change will be given. Cash value 0.0001p

code: PATGENVOU

In case of difficulty in obtaining copies, please contact Spring Harvest direct at info@springharvest.org or on 01825 769111